LAND AND PEOPLE
IN THE NORTHERN PLAINS TRANSITION AREA

Land and People in the
Northern Plains Transition Area

HOWARD W. OTTOSON

ELEANOR M. BIRCH

PHILIP A. HENDERSON

A. H. ANDERSON

UNIVERSITY OF NEBRASKA PRESS · LINCOLN

Publishers on the Plains

UNP

Copyright © 1966 by the University of Nebraska Press

All rights reserved

Library of Congress Catalog Card Number: 66-10878

Manufactured in the United States of America

Preface

THE LITERATURE about the Great Plains is growing, particularly with the renewed interest in the region associated with the recent anniversary of the passage of the Homestead Act. This volume is not primarily concerned with the broad reaches of the Great Plains, however; it focuses on the region of physical and economic transition between the more intensive corn-belt type of agriculture in the eastern fringe of the Plains and upon the extensive wheat or ranching regions of the High Plains.

Our interest in the transition area evolved in several ways. One of the authors spent his early years on a farm in south-central Nebraska, where he experienced transition-area farming at its best and its worst. During the drought years of the 1930's, a colleague, Mr. T. S. Thorfinnson, had investigated several transition-area counties, such as Hand County, South Dakota, and Boone County, Nebraska, and has stimulated us with his continuing curiosity about their more recent economic adjustments. We frequently observed that net incomes on farms in the transition area of Nebraska were low compared to those in areas to the west and to the east. One of the authors, A. H. Anderson, applied the concept of an institutional lag to the transition area, suggesting the hypothesis that the problem of inadequate farm size was mirrored in poorly adapted social institutions. Finally, Dean W. V. Lambert of the University of Nebraska College of Agriculture and Home Economics encouraged us to develop a project which would explore the possibilities for resource adjustments in the transition area. The drought that started in 1954, and became serious in 1955, provided additional incentive for undertaking such a project.

Although we have not intended it primarily as a history, the first part of this book sets the historical background. The problems which we have examined are rooted in the past—particularly in the land policies of the nineteenth century—and in the resulting waves of settlement as new lands were taken up in the Northern Plains. A historical review gives one a sense of the ebbs and flows of human events, an idea of the kinds of innovations required of people during the development of the area, and an appreciation for the economic and social progress which has been made.

In Part II we have dealt with the present, narrowing our attention—for purposes of analysis—to a pilot area in central Nebraska. Our intention here is to evaluate the present state of social development of this area, for it is to some extent representative of the broader transition area of the four states of the Northern Plains, at least in qualitative terms. We have tried not to work narrowly as economists, and have included in our analysis topics which might be classified as sociology or political science. Certain pitfalls are inherent in such an attempt, which we were only dimly aware of at the beginning, and which we did not succeed in completely avoiding. For example, conceptual limitations become obvious when one ventures outside the customary confines of his own discipline. Also, the range of topics in which one can interest himself exceeds his energy and resources.

Thus we analyzed the differential development of the Northern Plains and other regions. We dealt at some length with farm organization, size, efficiency, and income. Curiosity then led us to the matter of capital accumulation by farmers, and the large topic of farm credit and finance. When one considers adjustments in farm size as a means of increasing income, he finds himself thinking about population dynamics and social relations between farmers and the rest of the community. Therefore, we have considered such topics as the movement of population in the transition area, the nature of public services available, and the present situation of the small town.

Part III is an excursion into the future. We assume that there is no fundamental reason why the transition area cannot be as economically viable and as socially satisfying as any other region. In a specialized agricultural region, one starts with the farms and works out from them. We have conjectured about the future size of farms and the number of farm people, and about the size of towns and the number of townspeople. With estimates of future population and notions of the economics of size for public and private services, one can speculate about feasible alternatives—as far as public services are concerned—and about the nature of the private sector at the level of the small town and its economic area. One feels impelled to inject a note of caution at this point. It is obviously impossible to predict what is to come and foolhardy to make recommendations which do not rest on firm assumptions about the future; however, a research person can start discussions by his suggestions, and this is our hope for this section.

This study—which was carried on in the University of Nebraska Agricultural Experiment Station as Project 535, Adjustments Needed in the Use of Resources in the Transition Area of Nebraska—was made possible by a research grant from Resources for the Future, Inc., Washington, D.C.

We are indebted to many persons for assistance of various kinds. The study would have been impossible without the time and energy of the other members of our research group: Loyd Fischer and Roger Willsie. The counsel and encouragement of Marion Clawson of Resources for the Future, Inc., was crucial during the whole study. Several graduate students contributed at various times: Donald Novotny, Jerrold Stark, Joseph Havelka, Jerry Flaherty, Keith Young, Daryl Raitt, Dale Thompson, and Robert Eikleberry. Mrs. Wayne Collings was indefatigable in reviewing the literature, and Wayne Collings was most cooperative in providing us the services of the University of Nebraska College of Agriculture Library.

We are grateful to a large number of people for advice and suggestions, including T. S. Thorfinnson, USDA; Joseph Ackerman, Farm Foundation; the members of the Great Plains Resource Economics Committee, who sponsored a workshop in 1956 for our benefit; John Muehlbeier, Secretary of the Great Plains Agricultural Council;

Andrew Aandahl, Soil Survey, SCS; and various members of the Department of Agricultural Economics at the University of Nebraska. We also appreciated the cooperation and efforts of the members of the Nebraska Transition Area Committee, who spent long hours in studying the problems of the transition area and their solutions. We have appreciated the encouragement and support for the project by Dean W. V. Lambert and Director (and later Dean) E. F. Frolik of the College of Agriculture and Home Economics, University of Nebraska. We are also grateful to Reuben Gustafson, formerly Director and now a member of the Board of Resources for the Future, Inc., and to Otto H. Liebers, also a member of the Board. The review comments of Professors Layton Thompson of Montana State College and Rex Rehnberg of Colorado State University were most helpful.

Finally, we owe our thanks to the secretarial staff of the Agricultural Economics Department, University of Nebraska, and particularly to Mrs. Elsie Westerberg, who bore the brunt of the task of typing the manuscripts.

HOWARD W. OTTOSON
ELEANOR M. BIRCH
PHILIP A. HENDERSON
A. H. ANDERSON

Contents

LAND AND PEOPLE IN THE
NORTHERN PLAINS TRANSITION AREA

CHAPTER 1

Introduction

PROBABLY no part of the country has had more economic ups and downs than the Great Plains. Since white men first set foot on the Plains, the area has been a source of mystery, romance, wealth, poverty, and frustration. Optimism and pessimism have alternated as men poured time and treasure into the region with little caution and less knowledge, only to be frustrated by natural and economic forces.

Rain and drought, prosperity and depression have affected the various parts of the Plains in different ways. Some areas were hit very hard by adversity and the people had to adjust sharply or get out; others managed to survive with less drastic adjustments. Our story deals mainly with a particular part of the plains, the Northern Plains states: North Dakota, South Dakota, Nebraska, and Kansas; or, more specifically, we are interested in the problems of a unique economic region that crosses these states from north to south. It has no well-known popular name, but it is a transition zone between the more intensive farming area to the east and the extensive livestock or wheat farming areas to the west. We have therefore chosen to call it the "Plains transition area."

Our particular focus on this transition zone implies no lack of interest in the Great Plains as a whole. In fact, the history of the Plains is the history of our study area; and we must turn to the larger Plains picture for historical and geographical perspective. On the other hand, the Plains transition area is economically important in its own right, representing one-third of the population and land area of the four Northern Plains states, and over 7 percent of the population and 10 percent of the land area in the ten Great Plains states. The agricultural problems of the transition area are important in their own rights; and its institutional problems are found over the whole region of the Plains.

The Plains transition area has some unique features. It is one of the most rural in the country, with the majority of its people classified as farmers. It has lagged behind other areas in resource adjustments and in farm income. Both the extensive farming areas to the west and the intensive ones to the east have higher income levels. From the earliest days of its settlement, the farmers in this area have tried to farm like their neighbors to the east. Indeed, at times this has seemed justifiable; the soils appear to be as easily tilled and as productive. When rainfall is adequate for intensive crop production, these lands can produce; but when rainfall is less abundant, the area

1

becomes more like those to the west—and the vulnerability of intensive farming on small farms is demonstrated anew. On this unstable agricultural base the corn-belt institutions—schools, churches, local government, commerce, roads—have never become adequately adjusted to their environment. Kraenzel minces no words:

> It is interesting that the residents of this border country look east, and shun the country to the west of them. They seem to take pride in their closeness to the humid region and to feel no loyalty or responsibility towards the semiarid area. This attitude and its results are like "cutting off the nose to spite the face," for it is in exactly this transition zone—that area in which people prefer to use the expression "subhumid" rather than "semiarid"—that the more disastrous consequences follow upon conditions of semiaridity. This is because the people of this area, and their institutions, are not prepared for such an eventuality.[1]

People who live there continue to ask questions about this area. They wonder how it can become economically competitive. They are concerned about the out-migration of population, equating this phenomenon with economic decline, something they feel should be stopped. They think about school reorganization, and wonder how far this should go in the interests of economy and better education. Nearly everyone would welcome some easy way to attract new industry, seeing in it a means of keeping population, providing employment, and generating additional income. The perennial question of crops versus grass faces the farmers, along with related questions of live-stock organization and size of farm. Our story is an attempt to increase knowledge and suggest some answers to these and other questions raised about this area. We shall point out both the likely and unlikely avenues for economic adjustment in its rural landscape.

Geographical Perspective

The Great Plains region includes one-fifth of the land area of the United States. Stretching from Canada almost to the Mexican border, it is about 1,300 miles in length and varies from 200 to 700 miles in width. It includes parts of ten states: North Dakota, South Dakota, Nebraska, Kansas, Oklahoma, Texas, New Mexico, Colorado, Wyoming, and Montana. It is equivalent in size to the part of the United States east of the Mississippi River.

The Rocky Mountains provide a distinct natural boundary for the Great Plains on the west; the eastern boundary is less definite. Several natural characteristics could be used to define the eastern limits; three of these are shown in Figure 1. First, the 20-inch rainfall line might at first glance be thought to represent the western limit of humid and subhumid agriculture; yet this is misleading, since evaporation increases as one goes from north to south along a given meridian. An "effective" rainfall line equivalent to 20 inches annually at the Canadian border—after adjustment for evaporation—drops southward from the northern border fairly close to the 98th meridian and east of the actual 20-inch line.

The boundaries of the Great Plains might also be defined through soil differences. To the east the soil becomes darker and the layer of lime accumulation goes deeper. The western boundary of the humid soils, where the accumulation disappears, is

[1] Carl Frederick Kraenzel, *The Great Plains in Transition* (Norman: University of Oklahoma Press, 1955), p. 16.

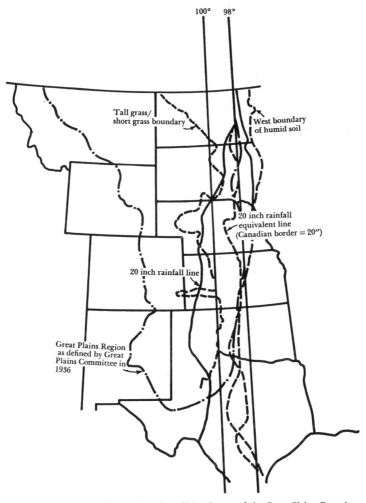

Based, in part, on *The Future of the Great Plains*, Report of the Great Plains Committee (U.S. Govt. Printing Office, 1936), p. 24.

FIG. 1. GREAT PLAINS REGION, WITH SOME CHARACTERISTICS OF
ITS EASTERN LIMITS

close to the 98th meridian from Texas to Kansas, and it then moves farther east as one goes north.

Finally, the boundary between the native tall-grass vegetation and the short grasses runs generally along the 100th meridian. It bulges west in Nebraska, and again in North Dakota.

As a rough approximation, the 98th meridian may be considered to be the eastern boundary of the Great Plains. Immediately to the west of this eastern boundary, in the four Northern Plains states, lies the transition area in which we are interested. It lies, roughly, between the 98th and 100th meridians. A closer approximation of its western boundary, from the standpoint of soil and land-use potential, is the boundary

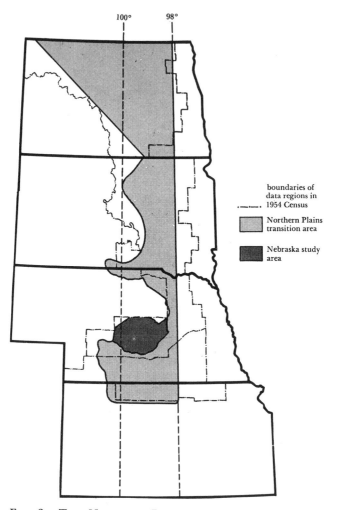

FIG. 2. THE NORTHERN PLAINS TRANSITION AREA, THE
ECONOMIC SUBREGIONS, AND THE NEBRASKA STUDY AREA

between the native tall grasses and the short grasses, excluding the Sandhills of
Nebraska. Thus defined, it is shown as the irregular shaded area in Figure 2. It is
wide in North Dakota, lying generally east of the Missouri in both of the Dakotas. It
lies east of the Sandhills in north-central Nebraska, then widens to the west, still
following the Sandhills boundary to the Platte River. Leaving the Sandhills south of
the Platte, it is again bounded by the tall-grass–short-grass line into Kansas. The
specialized winter wheat area in Kansas marks its southern limit below the first tier of
counties. The eastern boundary is the 20-inch effective rainfall line.

Our analysis has relied partly on data from the economic subregions and their
components, the economic areas, delineated by the U.S. Bureau of the Census in
1954. As can be seen in Figure 2, the boundaries of several subregions in the Northern
Plains states fit the transition area quite well. Also shown is the Nebraska study area in

which we conducted intensive study of farming problems that characterize the Plains transition area, and which was the second important source of data.

HOW THE TRANSITION AREA DEVELOPED

The history of the transition area is that of the settlement and development of the Plains. It is a fascinating tale whose lessons are not yet completely understood, even by its residents. The story starts with the Louisiana Purchase of 1803, which created an immediate need to explore the new territory. Accordingly, Lewis and Clark followed the Missouri River across the Plains country (1804–6), and they observed the effects of drought. Lieutenant Pike, traveling southwest to New Mexico (1806), saw the same conditions and advised settlers to stay to the east of the Missouri River. Major Long followed (1819–20); he traveled up the Platte River, thought the area uninhabitable by farmers, and coined the term "the Great American Desert," which for many years served as the popular nickname for the Plains.

Fur traders and trappers followed explorers, and the army came in to maintain a semblance of order. The Plains became a land to cross. The army crossed it on the way to Mexico; miners crossed it on the way to California. Mormons pushed their handcarts across it to Utah, and other pioneers drove their wagons across it to Oregon and Washington. With the settlement of people on the Pacific coast, transcontinental transportation and communication became necessary and quickly followed. Steamboats appeared on the Missouri. Freighters and stage lines carried people and freight along the pioneer trails; communication was speeded—momentarily—by the Pony Express in 1860, and then by the telegraph in 1861. In their wake came the railroads, linking the east and west with steel bands. Heavily subsidized, the railroads not only enhanced transportation and communications but facilitated the consolidation of the territorial expansion that had been taking place since 1800.

What of Plains settlement? With all of the coming and going across the Plains, surprisingly few people actually settled there in this early period. The first attempt, coming rapidly and without fanfare, was the occupation of the region by cattlemen, starting in 1866–67; their reign was relatively unchallenged until 1880. In the popular literature, the fundamental aspects of this story have not been widely told. We have heard about wealthy, powerful cattle barons who persecuted defenseless homesteaders—and any young television fan can recognize the "bad guys" in this story—but the unaided adaptation of the cattlemen to the Plains environment has been recognized only recently. Yet a more permanent occupation was on the way, more nearly in line with national policies of the period. The Kansas-Nebraska Act of 1854 opened these two states to settlement, and the land was occupied by farmers, up to the 98th meridian, by 1870. There settlement paused, despite the Homestead Act of 1862. Webb gives us the reasons.

> The Great Plains offered such a contrast to the region east of the ninety-eighth meridian, the region with which American civilization had been familiar until about 1840, as to bring about a marked change in the ways of pioneering and living. For two centuries American pioneers had been working out a technique for the utilization of the humid regions east of the Mississippi River. They had found solutions for their problems and were conquering the

frontier at a steadily accelerating rate. Then in the early nineteenth century they crossed the Mississippi and came out on the Great Plains, an environment with which they had had no experience. The result was a complete though temporary breakdown of the machinery and ways of pioneering. They began to make adjustments. . . .

As one contrasts the civilization of the Great Plains with that of the eastern timberland, one sees what may be called an institutional *fault* (comparable to a geological fault) running from middle Texas to Illinois or Dakota, roughly following the ninety-eighth meridian. At this *fault* the ways of life and of living changed. Practically every institution that was carried across it was either broken and remade or else greatly altered. The ways of travel, the weapons, the methods of tilling the soil, the plows and other agricultural implements, and even the laws themselves were modified. When people first crossed this line they did not immediately realize the imperceptible change that had taken place in their environment; nor, more is the tragedy, did they foresee the full consequences which that change was to bring in their own characters and in their modes of life.[2]

There were no "road signs" or other landmarks at the 98th meridian to warn people about the strange land they were entering. In fact, the boundary to the Plains is a belt that does not remain fixed but meanders east or west with the weather. Major Powell thought the 100th meridian marked the limit of customary farming. At any rate, settlers who crossed into the Plains transition area felt no pressure to adjust suddenly or completely.

The settlement of the Plains states after 1870 was a sudden, reckless, awe-inspiring thing. Between that year and 1890, when the first phase halted, the population of the Plains states increased by more than 2.5 million. Several factors affected the course of this phase of settlement.

One basic influence was the land laws. The Homestead Act, giving people the right to file a claim on 160 acres of unappropriated public land and to "prove it" by five years of residence, was the result of a long struggle over the issue of free land. On one side were people like Alexander Hamilton, who thought the government should follow a conservative policy in the disposition of its public lands since land sales could provide an important source of revenue for the new federal government. On the other side were followers of Thomas Jefferson, who visualized a United States based on an agrarian economy, and who therefore favored a generous land policy. This great debate raged for three-quarters of a century. Then, in the election of 1860, Lincoln's platform included a proposal for a homestead act which won him support from western farmers—and, many historians believe, the election. The resulting Homestead Act, in 1862, signaled the victory of the free-land forces. But, though the 160-acre homestead was well adapted to the farming methods of the humid areas, it was ill advised when applied to the land west of the 98th meridian.

The commutation provision of the Homestead Act led to the exploitation of the cheap land by speculators or others who had no intention of operating it. The Timber Culture Act of 1873 and the Desert Land Act give little evidence of increased congressional knowledge concerning the resources of the west. However, the Kincaid Act of 1904, the Enlarged Homestead Act of 1909, and the Stock-raising Homestead Act of 1916 belatedly recognized that land resources in the Plains are not uniform, and

[2] Walter Prescott Webb, *The Great Plains* (New York: Grosset & Dunlap, 1931), pp. 8–9. Reprinted through the courtesy of Blaisdell Publishing Co., a division of Ginn & Company.

that the earlier legislation had ignored the differences between the humid and the Plains regions.

Other factors were operating. Over 91 million acres of land were given to the railroads after 1850 by the federal government (not all of it in the Plains) as a subsidy to support their construction operations across the country. For those to whom this figure is undramatic, it represents nearly twice the farm land in Nebraska. Additional land was provided by the states. About 17 percent of the land in Nebraska was given to the railroads, which became vigorous, supremely optimistic promoters of settlement—with immigration departments not only in this country but also in Europe. To their efforts must be added those of the land departments of the several states, which were only slightly less vociferous in extolling the farming opportunities in the prairie areas as they worked to dispose of the "educational" lands they had received and to build up their respective populations.

There was a "human supply" side to settlement, too. Young men released from the army at the close of the Civil War were eager to start farming. A large influx of immigrants provided another part of the supply of potential homesteaders in the prairie region.

Technology also played its role in settlement. We cannot overlook the enhanced control of nature represented in wire fences, the Colt revolver, windmills, the steel plow, the reaper, the harrow, and other implements.

The rapid settlement that occurred after 1870 was abetted by a series of wet years between 1878 and 1886. What more could a man want than good soil and rain? Indeed, the old term "American Desert" was relegated to a derided folklore. It had been "shown" by the best authorities, including Professor Aughey of the University of Nebraska, that rainfall followed the plow, and would increase with the planting of trees! Even the steel rails of the new railroads were said to attract their portion of increased rainfall. The voices of a few, such as Major Powell and Cyrus Thomas, were raised in protest, but they were largely crying in the wilderness, so enthusiastic was the temper of the times.

As rapidly as they settled, the people set up their institutions—towns, townships, schools, and counties. They laid out roads along section lines. In establishing these institutions they laid the basis for the struggle against the costs of local government that has characterized the Plains area ever since. By 1890, most of Kansas and Nebraska had been settled by homesteaders, as had South Dakota to the Missouri River and North Dakota in the Red River Valley.

It could have been different. We can, if we wish, contemplate the effects on settlement policy of a more thoughtful approach. Would it have helped to inventory and classify land resources in the Plains before rushing in pell-mell? What would have happened had the land been distributed by the federal government through sale rather than homestead? Would this have checked speculation and encouraged the serious, experienced settler? How about homesteads differing in size, whose acreage would depend on land productivity? What about abandoning the rectangular survey, as Powell proposed? Could we have been somewhat more realistic about the future population potentials of these areas before setting up the county and state units we now have? (Before rejecting this suggestion too hastily, let us remember that Texas has the privilege of subdividing into four parts but has not yet chosen to do so.)

The melancholy fact about the above measures is that most of them had been proposed before heavy settlement started. There is no evidence that they were taken seriously by most people. The lack of knowledge that characterized the movement of millions of people, the dedication of their lives, and the commitment of their families and resources to new environments is almost fantastic. There was a general air of incredulity about what little knowledge was available; hence it was disregarded. It *could* have been different.

We look at the past not to mourn nor to pass undue judgment; we study it principally to understand its lessons and to apply them constructively. However, we have not yet shown complete willingness to use available knowledge in the solution of unsolved problems, even to the present day.

ADJUSTMENTS TAKE PLACE

The new settlements were tested without delay. Grasshoppers, chinch bugs, hail, drought, and blizzards combined to plague them. Low prices for farm products compounded their difficulties. They were forced to adjust. In some areas settlers emigrated as rapidly as they had come, and there occurred the phenomenon of covered wagons going east. The area west of the 98th meridian suffered most as population declined and size of farms increased. It was a period of adjustment by individuals, since no tradition of governmental responsibility in affairs of these kinds had yet developed. However, the disasters of the 1890's were viewed as abnormalities and credited to the whims of fate rather than to the errors of men. They were quickly forgotten as the rains came again and as farming moved into its "parity period," the "golden era" of the early 1900's.

With the turn of the century, the history of the Northern Plains states diverged somewhat from that of the rest of the Plains as the differential characteristics of the area became more clearly discernible. This recent history is better known. The golden era was a period of farm prosperity, of the completion of settlement in the Dakotas, and of renewed optimism. With the coming of World War I, the agriculture of the area was mobilized and the slogan was "Food will win the war." Mechanization and the purchase of land at inflationary prices left the farmers vulnerable in new ways to the hazards of climate and prices. In the 1930's, disasters struck again—the not unfamiliar drought and low prices. Human hardships reached new depths as the economic base for living crumbled away. Again people were called upon to adjust, but this time with help from federal programs and agencies. Once again war followed —and rain, good prices, and new demands for food. When peace returned, prairie people anxiously examined recently passed landmarks for clues in answer to the question "Will it happen again?" It didn't; a new phenomenon, peacetime foreign aid programs, provided an additional source of demand for food. As if that were not enough, the Korean incident provided a further basis for the farm prosperity, which lasted until 1952.

THE FUTURE LIES IN OUR HANDS

The transition area, and the Plains generally, received another warning after 1952, however. It was a sobering experience. The warning came in the form of a drought and falling cattle prices, of a price-cost squeeze and storage stocks of wheat and corn. People reacted to the warning by "adjusting out" of some areas; and the federal government reacted with new programs. It was a disquieting time. The rest of the economy remained prosperous, providing opportunities for the people who left the region.

But what about those who remained? The rates of growth of the various economic sectors have not been similar. Such rural areas as the Sandhills of Nebraska, the wheat areas of western Kansas, and the ranch area of the western Dakotas have forged ahead in achieving desirable adjustments between people and resources, as measured by the criteria of income and living levels. This is also true of such areas as the Red River Valley of North and South Dakota, and the Missouri bottoms of Nebraska. On the other hand, farming in the transition area has fallen behind in relative terms. Meanwhile, the larger towns in the Plains have been growing while the smaller towns have been shrinking. Probably most serious of all is the slow rate of progress by some of the rural institutions that are based on the agricultural industry.

During this centennial decade of the Homestead Act, it seems particularly appropriate that we pause and take stock to see where we have been in the Northern Plains and the transition area, to examine the features of the present situation, and to contemplate future courses of action. In brief, these are the aims of this book.

Part I

HOW THE AREA DEVELOPED AND THE OUTSIDE FACTORS THAT AFFECTED IT

CHAPTER 2

Land and Climate of the Northern Plains

MANY of the hardships the first Plains settlers faced were due to the climate. These difficulties were compounded by only scanty knowledge of either climate or soils. Many mistakes were made, but there is little reason to believe that succeeding generations would have made any fewer under similar circumstances.

The history of the settlement and development of the Plains is best understood against the background of the area's natural features. Therefore, this chapter will review the climatic and soil characteristics of the Plains in general.

Few areas have been the subject of more conflicting statements than the Plains, since the time of earliest exploration. Part of the divergence between these expressed opinions was undoubtedly due to personal differences in evaluation of a given set of circumstances. Nevertheless, many of these apparently conflicting stories about the Plains were not truly contradictory; they may well have been accurate observations, but of different locations or of different times.

Lieutenant Zebulon M. Pike, who traveled west along the Republican River in 1806 and thence to Santa Fe, expressed the opinion that this area of "barren soil, parched and dried up for eight months in the year" would "become in time equally celebrated as the sandy deserts [*sic*] of Africa."[1]

Major Stephen H. Long, upon returning from his expedition to the Rockies in 1820, wrote:

> In regard to this extensive section of country [between the Missouri River and the Rocky Mountains], I do not hesitate in giving the opinion, that it is almost wholly unfit for cultivation, and of course uninhabitable by a people depending on agriculture for their subsistence.

Dr. Edwin James, who accompanied Major Long and who served as chronicler of the expedition, stated that he had "no fear of giving too unfavourable an account" of the region, believing that it was "an unfit residence for any but a nomad population," and that he hoped the area would remain forever "the unmolested haunt of the native hunter, the bison, and the jackall."[2] On the other hand, geographer Trewartha suggested that

---

[1] James C. Olson, *History of Nebraska* (Lincoln: University of Nebraska Press, 1955), p. 3.
[2] *Ibid.*

This is a region of most unusual natural potentialities. No other region of the earth of equal size is so well endowed physically—in surface configuration, soil, and climate—for agricultural use. Drought is the one serious natural handicap. . . . Never before had white settlers entered into such a "promised land," and never can they again, for no such frontiers remain.[3]

Thornthwaite wrote:

In a desert, you know what to expect of the climate and plan accordingly. The same is true of the humid regions. Men have been badly fooled by the semi-arid regions because they are sometimes humid, sometimes desert, and sometimes a cross between the two.[4]

Cyrus Thomas, one of the early explorers, astutely observed that

The troublesome factor in the great problem of the development of the agricultural capacity of the vast Western Plains is the supply of water. Furnish this, and the fertile prairies and valleys east of the Mississippi will soon find a strong rival contending with them in the grain marts of the world for precedence. Furnish this, and the "Great American Desert" of geographers will soon become one mighty field of flowing grain.[5]

The early settlers and legislators had little knowledge of the area. Records were not available to support or disprove reports that drifted back to the more thickly populated areas. The confusion created by seeming contradictions was augmented by the purposeful claims and glowing stories put forth by the area's promoters. It is little wonder that the farming patterns first established did not fit; nor is it too surprising that legislation affecting the settlement of the area was ill conceived.

On the other hand one can marvel at the rare insight displayed by men like Major J. W. Powell[6] and Cyrus Thomas[7] in their writings concerning the area. Few people today demonstrate as keen an understanding as these men apparently had of its natural characteristics and of the way they affect policies for the area.

Except for the very early years, during which white men were chiefly interested in furs and hides, the Plains area has been considered largely from the viewpoint of its potential for agriculture. Before the introduction of some of the newer developments in agriculture, the prosperity of farming or ranching depended largely on the inherent productivity of the soils and on the amount and distribution of precipitation.

SOILS OF THE NORTHERN PLAINS

As Thomas and Trewartha indicate, the Plains possess soils generally recognized as being among the most productive in the nation (see Figure 3), but this is not universally true of the Plains as a whole. According to Bennett, Kenney, and Chapline:

[3] Glenn T. Trewartha, "Climate and Settlement of the Subhumid Lands," *Climate and Man* (USDA Yearbook of Agriculture, 1941), p. 167.

[4] C. W. Thornthwaite, "Climate and Settlement of the Great Plains," *Climate and Man* (USDA Yearbook of Agriculture, 1941), p. 177.

[5] James C. Malin, "The Agricultural Regionalism of Trans-Mississippi West as Delineated by Cyrus Thomas," *Agricultural History* (January, 1947), p. 211.

[6] Author of several proposals and congressional bills directed at land and water use in the 1870's and 1880's. See Kraenzel, *The Great Plains in Transition*, pp. 292–99.

[7] Entomologist and botanist on the U.S. geological and geographical survey of the territories.

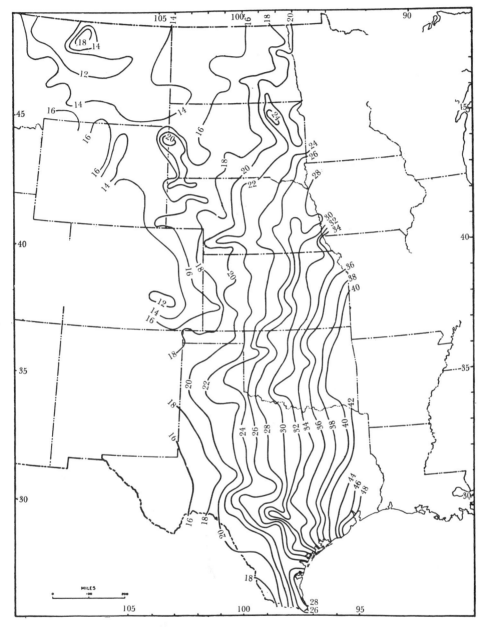

Source: *The Future of the Great Plains*, p. 26.

Fig. 5. Average Annual Precipitation in the Plains for a 40-year Period, 1895–1934 (in Inches)

19

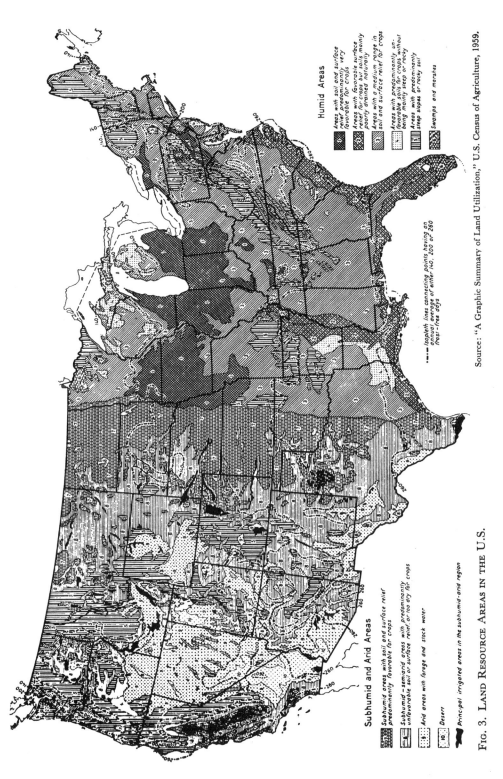

Subhumid and Arid Areas

▨ Subhumid areas with soil and surface relief predominantly favorable for crops

▤ Subhumid-semiarid areas with predominantly unfavorable soil or surface relief, or too dry for crops

▦ Arid areas with forage and stock water

□ Desert

◤ Principal irrigated areas in the subhumid-arid region

Humid Areas

■ Areas with soil and surface relief predominantly very favorable for crops

▧ Areas with favorable surface relief for crops but soils mainly poorly drained naturally

▥ Areas with a medium range in soil and surface relief for crops

▨ Areas with predominantly unfavorable soils for crops without being mainly steep and rocky

▦ Areas with predominantly steep slopes or rocky soil

▩ Swamps and marshes

--- Isopleth lines connecting points having an annual average of either 140, 200 or 260 frost-free days

Source: "A Graphic Summary of Land Utilization," U.S. Census of Agriculture, 1959.

FIG. 3. LAND RESOURCE AREAS IN THE U.S.

15

The soils of the Great Plains have a superficial appearance of uniformity, particularly on the more level lands. They vary widely in their productivity, however, even within small areas. While they are generally fertile, they exhibit wide diversity in their texture, their depth, and their water-holding capacity. Almost any of them will produce fairly good crops in wet years, but in dry years only those that absorb and hold large quantities of water and resist wind erosion can be farmed successfully.[8]

A large proportion of the land in the area is relatively flat to gently rolling, with dark-brown to black soils that contain a relatively large amount of organic matter, that are almost neutral in acidity, generally well drained, and inherently quite productive. For the most part, these soils would be included in capability classes II and III.[9] Included under such a dual description would be the Holdrege, Hall, Crete, and Hastings soils in central Nebraska and north-central Kansas; the Hayes soils of central Kansas; and the Barnes soils and some of the Williams and Morton soils of North and South Dakota. To a large extent, these are used for crop production.

Interspersed with soils of the first group are much smaller areas of soils with poor surface and subsurface drainage. Such soils may be and are cultivated in the drier years, but, because of standing water, they cannot be cultivated in the wetter years. There are also areas of shallow soils overlying shale, sandstone, gravel, or sand. These tend to be droughty.

Scattered throughout the region are rather large areas of steeply rolling to hilly topography. These soils, especially when cultivated, are highly susceptible to water erosion. Much, and in some cases all, surface soil has been lost. Free lime can frequently be found at or near the surface. Their productivity is quite low; consequently, a large part of these soils is used for pasture. In general, they fall into capability classes IV and VI, being marginal for cultivation; and in many instances they are best suited for pasture purposes in the long run. Included in this group might

[8] John B. Bennett, F. R. Kenney, and W. R. Chapline, "The Great Plains and Other Dry Land Farming Regions," *Soils and Men* (USDA Yearbook of Agriculture, 1938), p. 69.

[9] *Class I.* Very good land that can be cultivated safely and easily with ordinary farming methods.

Class II. Land that can be cultivated safely with moderate conservation treatment. These soils may be slightly erodible or may have water or climate problems.

Class III. Soils with considerable limitations in use and that require intensive conservation treatments. Erosion, droughtiness, excessive wetness, overflow, or salinity may be the cause of the problem.

Class IV. Soils that are severely limited in use. They can be cultivated only occasionally and with extreme care. These soils may be erodible, droughty, wet, overflowed, or saline, so that the kinds of cultivated crops that can be grown—as well as the number of years favorable for crop production—are very limited.

Class V. Nearly level land that is best suited to permanent vegetation. These soils are often stony, wet, and subject to damaging overflow, or have a short growing season.

Class VI. Land that is best suited for grazing or forestry, with minor limitations. These soils are usually steeply sloping; some *Class VI* land may be severely eroded, shallow, wet, subject to damaging overflow, or droughty.

Class VII. Soils in this class are severely limited in use. The size of the conservation problems exceeds those in *Class VI.* They may be steep, stony, shallow, droughty, wet, subject to damaging overflow, or eroded. These soils are best protected by natural vegetation and limited use.

Class VIII. Very steep and rocky, sandy, or wet land. Useful for wildlife food-and-shelter areas or for recreational or water-yielding purposes. Not suited for commercial production of crops.

Helmut Kohnke and Anson R. Bertrand, *Soil Conservation* (New York: McGraw-Hill Book Company, 1959), pp. 153–54.

be the Colby soils of central Nebraska, a large part of the Boyd and Holt soils of South Dakota and Nebraska, the Barneville soils of North Dakota, and some of the hilly phases of Hayes soils in Kansas.

In addition, there are miscellaneous soils—especially along streams—such as those containing alkali outcrops, gravelly and sandy soils, alluvial soils, heavy clay (gumbo), and other soils of minor importance.

Practically all these soils have been developed under a mixed tall- and short-grass vegetation. Native vegetation included only a very few trees along streams.

Parent material of soils in the area varies greatly. A considerable portion of the soils in Nebraska and Kansas is developed from loess material. To the north, many of the soils are developed from shale, sandstone, and glacial material.

Throughout the area there is danger of wind erosion in dry years if care is not exercised in maintaining some cover. This is especially true of the sandier soils.

CLIMATE OF THE NORTHERN PLAINS

General Description

Briefly stated, the climate of the Northern Plains is characterized by low and variable precipitation, most of which occurs during the growing season; by low humidity; great extremes between summer and winter temperatures; relatively high wind velocity; high evaporation (in relation to rainfall); rather frequent occurrences of drought; a tendency for wet and dry years to occur in sequence; a tendency toward violent storms in the form of rain, hail, tornadoes, blizzards, and driving winds; and by sudden changes of temperature. Few words describe the climate of the Plains as well as *variable* and *uncertain*. These characteristics have been amply demonstrated by weather records since the time of settlement (see Figure 4).

Variability is one of the most marked characteristics of the area. However, the problems of farming in the area do not stem as much from the actual amount of the variation in precipitation as they do from the fact that these variations occur around a quantity that is critical to the needs of crops which farmers try to produce. In periods with above-average rainfall or with better-than-average distribution relative to the critical needs of crops, yields have been satisfactory and sometimes excellent. In periods with less-than-average rainfall or with poor distribution of it, yields tend to fall off sharply. In extreme instances, crops are a complete failure; abandonment of fall-seeded crops is high, and yields of harvested crops may be near zero. Sometimes crops are not harvested at all. Not only may the crop fail to produce grain, but there may be insufficient growth to warrant harvesting even for forage purposes. Whether harvested or not, the amount of vegetation cover is frequently not sufficient to prevent wind and water erosion.

In periods of above-average effective precipitation, crops highly susceptible to inadequate rainfall often turn out to be the most profitable. Each succeeding year of this kind convinces more farmers in the area to swing to the production of such crops. Unfortunately, it is not yet possible to predict accurately what weather conditions are going to prevail in the year or months ahead. Consequently, after prolonged favorable

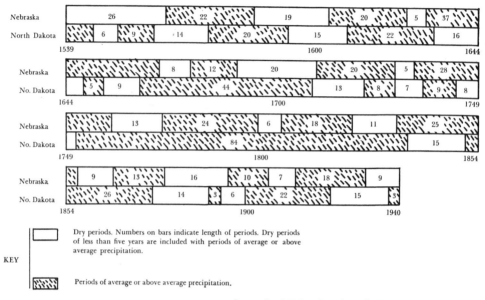

Dry periods. Numbers on bars indicate length of periods. Dry periods of less than five years are included with periods of average or above average precipitation.

KEY

Periods of average or above average precipitation.

Source: South Dakota Experiment Station Circular 132 (1957).

FIG. 4. DRY PERIODS OF FIVE OR MORE YEARS, 1539–1940, AS INDICATED BY TREE RINGS IN WESTERN NEBRASKA AND CENTRAL NORTH DAKOTA

periods, many farmers forget the uncertainties of weather and hence find themselves unprepared for a drought year.

Significance of Variable Climate

Owing to the rising costs of operation and the increasing relative importance of cash costs to total operating costs, farmers in the Plains are becoming more and more vulnerable to the uncertainties of weather and its consequences. Poor yields due to several unfavorable years in a row may soon tax a farm family's savings to a point where they may be forced out of business—much more quickly than twenty or thirty years ago.

Because of the limiting effect of moisture, farmers have not been able to use fertilizer as freely as their competitors in the cornbelt states to the east. If moisture is lacking at the time fertilizer must be applied, the amount of fertilizer that can justifiably be used is necessarily limited. Experimental work has clearly indicated that responses in yield to the use of fertilizer are closely related to the amount of moisture available.

Distribution of Precipitation and Its Effectiveness

The geographic distribution of average annual precipitation in the Plains is shown in Figure 5. Knowledge of the *average* precipitation alone, however, reveals very little about an area's practical capacity for agricultural production. *Reliability* of effective precipitation is more significant.

In the Northern Plains transition area, rainfall is anything but reliable—as illustrated in Figures 6 and 7. Years with less-than-average rainfall tend to be marked